# Personal Health Record Log Book

## My Medical Journal

Keeping your Medical History, Notes and Records
Safe, Up-to-Date, All in One Place and On Track.

## This Medical Journal Belongs To:

_____

# CONTENTS PAGE

# MY PERSONAL DETAILS

**FULL NAME:**

**DATE OF BIRTH:**                          **PLACE OF BIRTH:**

**HOME ADDRESS:**

**MOBILE TELEPHONE NUMBER:**

**HOME TELEPHONE NUMBER:**

**EMAIL ADDRESS:**

**BLOOD TYPE:**                             **GENOTYPE:**

**ALLERGIES:**

**HEIGHT:**

**CURRENT WEIGHT:**

**ORGAN DONAR:**

**ADDITIONAL INFORMATION:**

# MEDICAL CONTACT INFORMATION

## EMERGENCY CONTACT DETAILS -

RELATIONSHIP:

NAME:

PHONE:

ADDRESS:

EMAIL:

## PRIMARY PHYSICIAN -

PRACTICE:

NAME:

PHONE:

ADDRESS:

EMAIL:

## DENTIST -

PRACTICE:

NAME:

PHONE:

ADDRESS:

EMAIL:

## EYE SPECIALIST -

OPTICIANS:

NAME:

PHONE:

ADDRESS:

EMAIL:

## SPECIALIST -

PRACTICE:

NAME:

PHONE:

ADDRESS:

EMAIL:

## SPECIALIST -

PRACTICE:

NAME:

PHONE:

ADDRESS:

EMAIL:

# MEDICAL CONTACT INFORMATION

OTHER -

PRACTICE: _____

NAME: _____

PHONE: _____

ADDRESS: _____

_____

EMAIL: _____

OTHER -

PRACTICE: _____

NAME: _____

PHONE: _____

ADDRESS: _____

_____

EMAIL: _____

OTHER -

PRACTICE: _____

NAME: _____

PHONE: _____

ADDRESS: _____

_____

EMAIL: _____

OTHER -

OPTICIANS: _____

NAME: _____

PHONE: _____

ADDRESS: _____

_____

EMAIL: _____

OTHER -

PRACTICE: _____

NAME: _____

PHONE: _____

ADDRESS: _____

_____

EMAIL: _____

OTHER -

PRACTICE: _____

NAME: _____

PHONE: _____

ADDRESS: _____

_____

EMAIL: _____

# MEDICAL INSURANCE DETAILS

**COMPANY NAME:**

TYPE OF COVER:

POLICY NUMBER:

TELEPHONE NUMBER:

CONTACT NAME:

EMAIL ADDRESS:

ADDRESS:

WEBSITE:

**COMPANY NAME:**

TYPE OF COVER:

POLICY NUMBER:

TELEPHONE NUMBER:

CONTACT NAME:

EMAIL ADDRESS:

ADDRESS:

WEBSITE:

# MEDICAL INSURANCE DETAILS

**COMPANY NAME:**

TYPE OF COVER:

POLICY NUMBER:

TELEPHONE NUMBER:

CONTACT NAME:

EMAIL ADDRESS:

ADDRESS:

WEBSITE:

**COMPANY NAME:**

TYPE OF COVER:

POLICY NUMBER:

TELEPHONE NUMBER:

CONTACT NAME:

EMAIL ADDRESS:

ADDRESS:

WEBSITE:

# MEDICAL HISTORY RECORD

ONGOING HEALTH CONDITION:

FIRST DIAGNOSED:

DOCTOR'S INVOLVED:

TREATMENT PRESCRIBED:

ONGOING HEALTH CONDITION:

FIRST DIAGNOSED:

DOCTOR'S INVOLVED:

TREATMENT PRESCRIBED:

# MEDICAL HISTORY RECORD

ONGOING HEALTH CONDITION:

FIRST DIAGNOSED:

DOCTOR'S INVOLVED:

TREATMENT PRESCRIBED:

ONGOING HEALTH CONDITION:

FIRST DIAGNOSED:

DOCTOR'S INVOLVED:

TREATMENT PRESCRIBED:

# MEDICAL HISTORY RECORD

ONGOING HEALTH CONDITION:

FIRST DIAGNOSED:

DOCTOR'S INVOLVED:

TREATMENT PRESCRIBED:

ONGOING HEALTH CONDITION:

FIRST DIAGNOSED:

DOCTOR'S INVOLVED:

TREATMENT PRESCRIBED:

# MEDICAL HISTORY RECORD

ONGOING HEALTH CONDITION:

FIRST DIAGNOSED:

DOCTOR'S INVOLVED:

TREATMENT PRESCRIBED:

ONGOING HEALTH CONDITION:

FIRST DIAGNOSED:

DOCTOR'S INVOLVED:

TREATMENT PRESCRIBED:

# MEDICAL HISTORY RECORD

ONGOING HEALTH CONDITION:

FIRST DIAGNOSED:

DOCTOR'S INVOLVED:

TREATMENT PRESCRIBED:

ONGOING HEALTH CONDITION:

FIRST DIAGNOSED:

DOCTOR'S INVOLVED:

TREATMENT PRESCRIBED:

# MEDICAL HISTORY RECORD

ONGOING HEALTH CONDITION:

FIRST DIAGNOSED:

DOCTOR'S INVOLVED:

TREATMENT PRESCRIBED:

ONGOING HEALTH CONDITION:

FIRST DIAGNOSED:

DOCTOR'S INVOLVED:

TREATMENT PRESCRIBED:

# IMMUNIZATIONS / SHOTS

| DATE: | TYPE: | DOCTOR: | BOOSTER DUE: |
|-------|-------|---------|--------------|
|       |       |         |              |
|       |       |         |              |
|       |       |         |              |
|       |       |         |              |
|       |       |         |              |
|       |       |         |              |
|       |       |         |              |
|       |       |         |              |
|       |       |         |              |
|       |       |         |              |
|       |       |         |              |

# IMMUNIZATIONS / SHOTS

| DATE: | TYPE: | DOCTOR: | BOOSTER DUE: |
|-------|-------|---------|--------------|
|       |       |         |              |
|       |       |         |              |
|       |       |         |              |
|       |       |         |              |
|       |       |         |              |
|       |       |         |              |
|       |       |         |              |
|       |       |         |              |
|       |       |         |              |
|       |       |         |              |
|       |       |         |              |
|       |       |         |              |
|       |       |         |              |
|       |       |         |              |

# IMMUNIZATIONS / SHOTS

| DATE: | TYPE: | DOCTOR: | BOOSTER DUE: |
|-------|-------|---------|--------------|
|       |       |         |              |
|       |       |         |              |
|       |       |         |              |
|       |       |         |              |
|       |       |         |              |
|       |       |         |              |
|       |       |         |              |
|       |       |         |              |
|       |       |         |              |
|       |       |         |              |
|       |       |         |              |
|       |       |         |              |

# PRESCRIBED MEDICATION

NAME OF MEDICATION:

DATE STARTED:

DATE FINISHED:

DOSAGE:

DOSAGE TIMES:

SPECIAL INSTRUCTIONS:

REASON FOR MEDICATION:

ANY SIDE EFFECTS EXPERIENCED:

NAME OF PRESCRIBING PHYSICIAN:

CONTACT NUMBER FOR PHYSICIAN:

DESCRIPTION OF MEDICATION (SIZE, SHAPE, COLOR...)

PHARMACY CONTACT NUMBER:

REFILL NUMBER:

ANY ADDITIONAL INFORMATION / CHANGE TO DOSAGE:

# PRESCRIBED MEDICATION

NAME OF MEDICATION:

DATE STARTED:

DATE FINISHED:

DOSAGE:

DOSAGE TIMES:

SPECIAL INSTRUCTIONS:

REASON FOR MEDICATION:

ANY SIDE EFFECTS EXPERIENCED:

NAME OF PRESCRIBING PHYSICIAN:

CONTACT NUMBER FOR PHYSICIAN:

DESCRIPTION OF MEDICATION (SIZE, SHAPE, COLOR...)

PHARMACY CONTACT NUMBER:

REFILL NUMBER:

ANY ADDITIONAL INFORMATION / CHANGE TO DOSAGE:

# PRESCRIBED MEDICATION

NAME OF MEDICATION:

DATE STARTED:

DATE FINISHED:

DOSAGE:

DOSAGE TIMES:

SPECIAL INSTRUCTIONS:

REASON FOR MEDICATION:

ANY SIDE EFFECTS EXPERIENCED:

NAME OF PRESCRIBING PHYSICIAN:

CONTACT NUMBER FOR PHYSICIAN:

DESCRIPTION OF MEDICATION (SIZE, SHAPE, COLOR...)

PHARMACY CONTACT NUMBER:

REFILL NUMBER:

ANY ADDITIONAL INFORMATION / CHANGE TO DOSAGE:

# PRESCRIBED MEDICATION

NAME OF MEDICATION:

DATE STARTED:

DATE FINISHED:

DOSAGE:

DOSAGE TIMES:

SPECIAL INSTRUCTIONS:

REASON FOR MEDICATION:

ANY SIDE EFFECTS EXPERIENCED:

NAME OF PRESCRIBING PHYSICIAN:

CONTACT NUMBER FOR PHYSICIAN:

DESCRIPTION OF MEDICATION (SIZE, SHAPE, COLOR...)

PHARMACY CONTACT NUMBER:

REFILL NUMBER:

ANY ADDITIONAL INFORMATION / CHANGE TO DOSAGE:

# PRESCRIBED MEDICATION

NAME OF MEDICATION:

DATE STARTED:

DATE FINISHED:

DOSAGE:

DOSAGE TIMES:

SPECIAL INSTRUCTIONS:

REASON FOR MEDICATION:

ANY SIDE EFFECTS EXPERIENCED:

NAME OF PRESCRIBING PHYSICIAN:

CONTACT NUMBER FOR PHYSICIAN:

DESCRIPTION OF MEDICATION (SIZE, SHAPE, COLOR...)

PHARMACY CONTACT NUMBER:

REFILL NUMBER:

ANY ADDITIONAL INFORMATION / CHANGE TO DOSAGE:

# PRESCRIBED MEDICATION

NAME OF MEDICATION:

DATE STARTED:

DATE FINISHED:

DOSAGE:

DOSAGE TIMES:

SPECIAL INSTRUCTIONS:

REASON FOR MEDICATION:

ANY SIDE EFFECTS EXPERIENCED:

NAME OF PRESCRIBING PHYSICIAN:

CONTACT NUMBER FOR PHYSICIAN:

DESCRIPTION OF MEDICATION (SIZE, SHAPE, COLOR...)

PHARMACY CONTACT NUMBER:

REFILL NUMBER:

ANY ADDITIONAL INFORMATION / CHANGE TO DOSAGE:

# PRESCRIBED MEDICATION

NAME OF MEDICATION:

DATE STARTED:

DATE FINISHED:

DOSAGE:

DOSAGE TIMES:

SPECIAL INSTRUCTIONS:

REASON FOR MEDICATION:

ANY SIDE EFFECTS EXPERIENCED:

NAME OF PRESCRIBING PHYSICIAN:

CONTACT NUMBER FOR PHYSICIAN:

DESCRIPTION OF MEDICATION (SIZE, SHAPE, COLOR...)

PHARMACY CONTACT NUMBER:

REFILL NUMBER:

ANY ADDITIONAL INFORMATION / CHANGE TO DOSAGE:

# PRESCRIBED MEDICATION

NAME OF MEDICATION:

DATE STARTED:

DATE FINISHED:

DOSAGE:

DOSAGE TIMES:

SPECIAL INSTRUCTIONS:

REASON FOR MEDICATION:

ANY SIDE EFFECTS EXPERIENCED:

NAME OF PRESCRIBING PHYSICIAN:

CONTACT NUMBER FOR PHYSICIAN:

DESCRIPTION OF MEDICATION (SIZE, SHAPE, COLOR...)

PHARMACY CONTACT NUMBER:

REFILL NUMBER:

ANY ADDITIONAL INFORMATION / CHANGE TO DOSAGE:

# PRESCRIBED MEDICATION

NAME OF MEDICATION:

DATE STARTED:

DATE FINISHED:

DOSAGE:

DOSAGE TIMES:

SPECIAL INSTRUCTIONS:

REASON FOR MEDICATION:

ANY SIDE EFFECTS EXPERIENCED:

NAME OF PRESCRIBING PHYSICIAN:

CONTACT NUMBER FOR PHYSICIAN:

DESCRIPTION OF MEDICATION (SIZE, SHAPE, COLOR...)

PHARMACY CONTACT NUMBER:

REFILL NUMBER:

ANY ADDITIONAL INFORMATION / CHANGE TO DOSAGE:

# PRESCRIBED MEDICATION

NAME OF MEDICATION:

DATE STARTED:

DATE FINISHED:

DOSAGE:

DOSAGE TIMES:

SPECIAL INSTRUCTIONS:

REASON FOR MEDICATION:

ANY SIDE EFFECTS EXPERIENCED:

NAME OF PRESCRIBING PHYSICIAN:

CONTACT NUMBER FOR PHYSICIAN:

DESCRIPTION OF MEDICATION (SIZE, SHAPE, COLOR...)

PHARMACY CONTACT NUMBER:

REFILL NUMBER:

ANY ADDITIONAL INFORMATION / CHANGE TO DOSAGE:

# PRESCRIBED MEDICATION

NAME OF MEDICATION:

DATE STARTED:

DATE FINISHED:

DOSAGE:

DOSAGE TIMES:

SPECIAL INSTRUCTIONS:

REASON FOR MEDICATION:

ANY SIDE EFFECTS EXPERIENCED:

NAME OF PRESCRIBING PHYSICIAN:

CONTACT NUMBER FOR PHYSICIAN:

DESCRIPTION OF MEDICATION (SIZE, SHAPE, COLOR...)

PHARMACY CONTACT NUMBER:

REFILL NUMBER:

ANY ADDITIONAL INFORMATION / CHANGE TO DOSAGE:

# PRESCRIBED MEDICATION

NAME OF MEDICATION:

DATE STARTED:

DATE FINISHED:

DOSAGE:

DOSAGE TIMES:

SPECIAL INSTRUCTIONS:

REASON FOR MEDICATION:

ANY SIDE EFFECTS EXPERIENCED:

NAME OF PRESCRIBING PHYSICIAN:

CONTACT NUMBER FOR PHYSICIAN:

DESCRIPTION OF MEDICATION (SIZE, SHAPE, COLOR...)

PHARMACY CONTACT NUMBER:

REFILL NUMBER:

ANY ADDITIONAL INFORMATION / CHANGE TO DOSAGE:

# PRESCRIBED MEDICATION

NAME OF MEDICATION:

DATE STARTED:

DATE FINISHED:

DOSAGE:

DOSAGE TIMES:

SPECIAL INSTRUCTIONS:

REASON FOR MEDICATION:

ANY SIDE EFFECTS EXPERIENCED:

NAME OF PRESCRIBING PHYSICIAN:

CONTACT NUMBER FOR PHYSICIAN:

DESCRIPTION OF MEDICATION (SIZE, SHAPE, COLOR...)

PHARMACY CONTACT NUMBER:

REFILL NUMBER:

ANY ADDITIONAL INFORMATION / CHANGE TO DOSAGE:

# PRESCRIBED MEDICATION

NAME OF MEDICATION:

DATE STARTED:

DATE FINISHED:

DOSAGE:

DOSAGE TIMES:

SPECIAL INSTRUCTIONS:

REASON FOR MEDICATION:

ANY SIDE EFFECTS EXPERIENCED:

NAME OF PRESCRIBING PHYSICIAN:

CONTACT NUMBER FOR PHYSICIAN:

DESCRIPTION OF MEDICATION (SIZE, SHAPE, COLOR...)

PHARMACY CONTACT NUMBER:

REFILL NUMBER:

ANY ADDITIONAL INFORMATION / CHANGE TO DOSAGE:

# PRESCRIBED MEDICATION

NAME OF MEDICATION:

DATE STARTED:

DATE FINISHED:

DOSAGE:

DOSAGE TIMES:

SPECIAL INSTRUCTIONS:

REASON FOR MEDICATION:

ANY SIDE EFFECTS EXPERIENCED:

NAME OF PRESCRIBING PHYSICIAN:

CONTACT NUMBER FOR PHYSICIAN:

DESCRIPTION OF MEDICATION (SIZE, SHAPE, COLOR...)

PHARMACY CONTACT NUMBER:

REFILL NUMBER:

ANY ADDITIONAL INFORMATION / CHANGE TO DOSAGE:

# MEDICAL APPOINTMENT PLANNER

| DATE | DOCTOR | REASON |
|------|--------|--------|
|      |        |        |
|      |        |        |
|      |        |        |
|      |        |        |
|      |        |        |
|      |        |        |
|      |        |        |
|      |        |        |
|      |        |        |
|      |        |        |
|      |        |        |
|      |        |        |

# MEDICAL APPOINTMENT PLANNER

| DATE | DOCTOR | REASON |
|------|--------|--------|
|      |        |        |
|      |        |        |
|      |        |        |
|      |        |        |
|      |        |        |
|      |        |        |
|      |        |        |
|      |        |        |
|      |        |        |
|      |        |        |
|      |        |        |
|      |        |        |
|      |        |        |

# MEDICAL APPOINTMENT PLANNER

| DATE | DOCTOR | REASON |
| --- | --- | --- |
| | | |
| | | |
| | | |
| | | |
| | | |
| | | |
| | | |
| | | |
| | | |
| | | |
| | | |
| | | |

# MEDICAL APPOINTMENT PLANNER

| DATE | DOCTOR | REASON |
|------|--------|--------|
|      |        |        |
|      |        |        |
|      |        |        |
|      |        |        |
|      |        |        |
|      |        |        |
|      |        |        |
|      |        |        |
|      |        |        |
|      |        |        |
|      |        |        |
|      |        |        |
|      |        |        |
|      |        |        |
|      |        |        |
|      |        |        |
|      |        |        |

# DOCTOR VISITS LOG

| DATE: | FOLLOW UP APPOINTMENT BOOKED? |
|---|---|

DOCTOR:

CLINIC / HOSPITAL:

REASON/PURPOSE:

OUTCOME / NOTES:

| DATE: | FOLLOW UP APPOINTMENT BOOKED? |
|---|---|

DOCTOR:

CLINIC / HOSPITAL:

REASON/PURPOSE:

OUTCOME / NOTES:

# DOCTOR VISITS LOG

DATE:

FOLLOW UP APPOINTMENT BOOKED?

DOCTOR:

CLINIC / HOSPITAL:

REASON/PURPOSE:

OUTCOME / NOTES:

DATE:

FOLLOW UP APPOINTMENT BOOKED?

DOCTOR:

CLINIC / HOSPITAL:

REASON/PURPOSE:

OUTCOME / NOTES:

# DOCTOR VISITS LOG

DATE:

FOLLOW UP APPOINTMENT BOOKED?

DOCTOR:

CLINIC / HOSPITAL:

REASON/PURPOSE:

OUTCOME / NOTES:

DATE:

FOLLOW UP APPOINTMENT BOOKED?

DOCTOR:

CLINIC / HOSPITAL:

REASON/PURPOSE:

OUTCOME / NOTES:

# DOCTOR VISITS LOG

DATE:

FOLLOW UP APPOINTMENT BOOKED?

DOCTOR:

CLINIC / HOSPITAL:

REASON/PURPOSE:

OUTCOME / NOTES:

DATE:

FOLLOW UP APPOINTMENT BOOKED?

DOCTOR:

CLINIC / HOSPITAL:

REASON/PURPOSE:

OUTCOME / NOTES:

# DOCTOR VISITS LOG

DATE:

FOLLOW UP APPOINTMENT BOOKED?

DOCTOR:

CLINIC / HOSPITAL:

REASON/PURPOSE:

OUTCOME / NOTES:

DATE:

FOLLOW UP APPOINTMENT BOOKED?

DOCTOR:

CLINIC / HOSPITAL:

REASON/PURPOSE:

OUTCOME / NOTES:

# DOCTOR VISITS LOG

DATE:

FOLLOW UP APPOINTMENT BOOKED?

DOCTOR:

CLINIC / HOSPITAL:

REASON/PURPOSE:

OUTCOME / NOTES:

DATE:

FOLLOW UP APPOINTMENT BOOKED?

DOCTOR:

CLINIC / HOSPITAL:

REASON/PURPOSE:

OUTCOME / NOTES:

# DOCTOR VISITS LOG

DATE:

FOLLOW UP APPOINTMENT
BOOKED?

DOCTOR:

CLINIC / HOSPITAL:

REASON/PURPOSE:

OUTCOME / NOTES:

DATE:

FOLLOW UP APPOINTMENT
BOOKED?

DOCTOR:

CLINIC / HOSPITAL:

REASON/PURPOSE:

OUTCOME / NOTES:

# DOCTOR VISITS LOG

| | FOLLOW UP APPOINTMENT BOOKED? |
|---|---|
| DATE: | |

DOCTOR:

CLINIC / HOSPITAL:

REASON/PURPOSE:

OUTCOME / NOTES:

| | FOLLOW UP APPOINTMENT BOOKED? |
|---|---|
| DATE: | |

DOCTOR:

CLINIC / HOSPITAL:

REASON/PURPOSE:

OUTCOME / NOTES:

# DOCTOR VISITS LOG

DATE: 

FOLLOW UP APPOINTMENT BOOKED?

DOCTOR:

CLINIC / HOSPITAL:

REASON/PURPOSE:

OUTCOME / NOTES:

DATE: 

FOLLOW UP APPOINTMENT BOOKED?

DOCTOR:

CLINIC / HOSPITAL:

REASON/PURPOSE:

OUTCOME / NOTES:

# DOCTOR VISITS LOG

| DATE: | FOLLOW UP APPOINTMENT BOOKED? |
|---|---|

DOCTOR:

CLINIC / HOSPITAL:

REASON/PURPOSE:

OUTCOME / NOTES:

| DATE: | FOLLOW UP APPOINTMENT BOOKED? |
|---|---|

DOCTOR:

CLINIC / HOSPITAL:

REASON/PURPOSE:

OUTCOME / NOTES:

# DOCTOR VISITS LOG

DATE:

FOLLOW UP APPOINTMENT BOOKED?

DOCTOR:

CLINIC / HOSPITAL:

REASON/PURPOSE:

OUTCOME / NOTES:

DATE:

FOLLOW UP APPOINTMENT BOOKED?

DOCTOR:

CLINIC / HOSPITAL:

REASON/PURPOSE:

OUTCOME / NOTES:

# DOCTOR VISITS LOG

DATE:

FOLLOW UP APPOINTMENT BOOKED?

DOCTOR:

CLINIC / HOSPITAL:

REASON/PURPOSE:

OUTCOME / NOTES:

DATE:

FOLLOW UP APPOINTMENT BOOKED?

DOCTOR:

CLINIC / HOSPITAL:

REASON/PURPOSE:

OUTCOME / NOTES:

# DOCTOR VISITS LOG

DATE:

FOLLOW UP APPOINTMENT
BOOKED?

DOCTOR:

CLINIC / HOSPITAL:

REASON/PURPOSE:

OUTCOME / NOTES:

DATE:

FOLLOW UP APPOINTMENT
BOOKED?

DOCTOR:

CLINIC / HOSPITAL:

REASON/PURPOSE:

OUTCOME / NOTES:

# DOCTOR VISITS LOG

| DATE: | FOLLOW UP APPOINTMENT BOOKED? |
|---|---|

**DOCTOR:**

**CLINIC / HOSPITAL:**

**REASON/PURPOSE:**

**OUTCOME / NOTES:**

| DATE: | FOLLOW UP APPOINTMENT BOOKED? |
|---|---|

**DOCTOR:**

**CLINIC / HOSPITAL:**

**REASON/PURPOSE:**

**OUTCOME / NOTES:**

# DOCTOR VISITS LOG

DATE:

FOLLOW UP APPOINTMENT BOOKED?

DOCTOR:

CLINIC / HOSPITAL:

REASON/PURPOSE:

OUTCOME / NOTES:

DATE:

FOLLOW UP APPOINTMENT BOOKED?

DOCTOR:

CLINIC / HOSPITAL:

REASON/PURPOSE:

OUTCOME / NOTES:

# DOCTOR VISITS LOG

DATE:                                    FOLLOW UP APPOINTMENT
                                         BOOKED?

DOCTOR:

CLINIC / HOSPITAL:

REASON/PURPOSE:

OUTCOME / NOTES:

DATE:                                    FOLLOW UP APPOINTMENT
                                         BOOKED?

DOCTOR:

CLINIC / HOSPITAL:

REASON/PURPOSE:

OUTCOME / NOTES:

# DOCTOR VISITS LOG

DATE:

FOLLOW UP APPOINTMENT BOOKED?

DOCTOR:

CLINIC / HOSPITAL:

REASON/PURPOSE:

OUTCOME / NOTES:

DATE:

FOLLOW UP APPOINTMENT BOOKED?

DOCTOR:

CLINIC / HOSPITAL:

REASON/PURPOSE:

OUTCOME / NOTES:

# DOCTOR VISITS LOG

DATE:                                         FOLLOW UP APPOINTMENT
                                              BOOKED?

DOCTOR:

CLINIC / HOSPITAL:

REASON/PURPOSE:

OUTCOME / NOTES:

DATE:                                         FOLLOW UP APPOINTMENT
                                              BOOKED?

DOCTOR:

CLINIC / HOSPITAL:

REASON/PURPOSE:

OUTCOME / NOTES:

# DOCTOR VISITS LOG

| DATE: | FOLLOW UP APPOINTMENT BOOKED? |
|---|---|

**DOCTOR:**

**CLINIC / HOSPITAL:**

**REASON/PURPOSE:**

**OUTCOME / NOTES:**

| DATE: | FOLLOW UP APPOINTMENT BOOKED? |
|---|---|

**DOCTOR:**

**CLINIC / HOSPITAL:**

**REASON/PURPOSE:**

**OUTCOME / NOTES:**

# DOCTOR VISITS LOG

DATE:

FOLLOW UP APPOINTMENT BOOKED?

DOCTOR:

CLINIC / HOSPITAL:

REASON/PURPOSE:

OUTCOME / NOTES:

DATE:

FOLLOW UP APPOINTMENT BOOKED?

DOCTOR:

CLINIC / HOSPITAL:

REASON/PURPOSE:

OUTCOME / NOTES:

# TEST RESULTS

| DATE: | TEST: | DOCTOR: | REASON FOR TEST: | RESULTS |
|-------|-------|---------|------------------|---------|
|       |       |         |                  |         |
|       |       |         |                  |         |
|       |       |         |                  |         |
|       |       |         |                  |         |
|       |       |         |                  |         |
|       |       |         |                  |         |
|       |       |         |                  |         |
|       |       |         |                  |         |
|       |       |         |                  |         |
|       |       |         |                  |         |
|       |       |         |                  |         |

# TEST RESULTS

| DATE: | TEST: | DOCTOR: | REASON FOR TEST: | RESULTS |
|-------|-------|---------|------------------|---------|
|       |       |         |                  |         |
|       |       |         |                  |         |
|       |       |         |                  |         |
|       |       |         |                  |         |
|       |       |         |                  |         |
|       |       |         |                  |         |
|       |       |         |                  |         |
|       |       |         |                  |         |
|       |       |         |                  |         |
|       |       |         |                  |         |
|       |       |         |                  |         |
|       |       |         |                  |         |

# TEST RESULTS

| DATE: | TEST: | DOCTOR: | REASON FOR TEST: | RESULTS |
|-------|-------|---------|------------------|---------|
|       |       |         |                  |         |
|       |       |         |                  |         |
|       |       |         |                  |         |
|       |       |         |                  |         |
|       |       |         |                  |         |
|       |       |         |                  |         |
|       |       |         |                  |         |
|       |       |         |                  |         |
|       |       |         |                  |         |
|       |       |         |                  |         |
|       |       |         |                  |         |
|       |       |         |                  |         |

# RECORD OF SURGERY

DATE OF SURGERY:

NAME OF SURGEON:

REASON FOR SURGERY:

OUTCOME / FURTHER NOTES:

DATE OF SURGERY:

NAME OF SURGEON:

REASON FOR SUGERY:

OUTCOME / FURTHER NOTES:

# RECORD OF SURGERY

DATE OF SURGERY:

NAME OF SURGEON:

REASON FOR SURGERY / PROCEDURE:

OUTCOME / FURTHER NOTES:

DATE OF SURGERY:

NAME OF SURGEON:

REASON FOR SUGERY / PROCEDURE:

OUTCOME / FURTHER NOTES:

# RECORD OF SURGERY

DATE OF SURGERY:

NAME OF SURGEON:

REASON FOR SURGERY / PROCEDURE:

OUTCOME / FURTHER NOTES:

DATE OF SURGERY:

NAME OF SURGEON:

REASON FOR SUGERY / PROCEDURE:

OUTCOME / FURTHER NOTES:

# RECORD OF SURGERY

DATE OF SURGERY:

NAME OF SURGEON:

REASON FOR SURGERY / PROCEDURE:

OUTCOME / FURTHER NOTES:

DATE OF SURGERY:

NAME OF SURGEON:

REASON FOR SUGERY / PROCEDURE:

OUTCOME / FURTHER NOTES:

# SYMPTOM TRACKER

| DATE SYMPTOM FIRST STARTED: | NATURE OF SYMPTOM: | MILD ☐ <br> MODERATE ☐ <br> SEVERE ☐ | CONTINUOUS OR INTERMITTENT |
|---|---|---|---|
| RELATED TO ONGOING HEALTH CONDITION? <br><br> YES / NO | VISIT TO PHYSICIAN / HOSPITAL? | MEDICATION PRESCRIBED: | NOTES: |

| DATE SYMPTOM FIRST STARTED: | NATURE OF SYMPTOM: | MILD <br> MODERATE <br> SEVERE | CONTINUOUS OR INTERMITTENT |
|---|---|---|---|
| RELATED TO ONGOING HEALTH CONDITION? <br><br> YES / NO | VISIT TO PHYSICIAN / HOSPITAL? | MEDICATION PRESCRIBED: | NOTES: |

| DATE SYMPTOM FIRST STARTED: | NATURE OF SYMPTOM: | MILD <br> MODERATE <br> SEVERE | CONTINUOUS OR INTERMITTENT |
|---|---|---|---|
| RELATED TO ONGOING HEALTH CONDITION? <br><br> YES / NO | VISIT TO PHYSICIAN / HOSPITAL? | MEDICATION PRESCRIBED: | NOTES: |

# SYMPTOM TRACKER

| DATE SYMPTOM FIRST STARTED: | NATURE OF SYMPTOM: | MILD ☐ MODERATE ☐ SEVERE ☐ | CONTINUOUS OR INTERMITTENT |
|---|---|---|---|
| RELATED TO ONGOING HEALTH CONDITION? YES / NO | VISIT TO PHYSICIAN / HOSPITAL? | MEDICATION PRESCRIBED: | NOTES: |

| DATE SYMPTOM FIRST STARTED: | NATURE OF SYMPTOM: | MILD MODERATE SEVERE | CONTINUOUS OR INTERMITTENT |
|---|---|---|---|
| RELATED TO ONGOING HEALTH CONDITION? YES / NO | VISIT TO PHYSICIAN / HOSPITAL? | MEDICATION PRESCRIBED: | NOTES: |

| DATE SYMPTOM FIRST STARTED: | NATURE OF SYMPTOM: | MILD MODERATE SEVERE | CONTINUOUS OR INTERMITTENT |
|---|---|---|---|
| RELATED TO ONGOING HEALTH CONDITION? YES / NO | VISIT TO PHYSICIAN / HOSPITAL? | MEDICATION PRESCRIBED: | NOTES: |

# SYMPTOM TRACKER

| DATE SYMPTOM FIRST STARTED: | NATURE OF SYMPTOM: | MILD ☐ MODERATE ☐ SEVERE ☐ | CONTINUOUS OR INTERMITTENT |
|---|---|---|---|
| RELATED TO ONGOING HEALTH CONDITION? YES / NO | VISIT TO PHYSICIAN / HOSPITAL? | MEDICATION PRESCRIBED: | NOTES: |

| DATE SYMPTOM FIRST STARTED: | NATURE OF SYMPTOM: | MILD MODERATE SEVERE | CONTINUOUS OR INTERMITTENT |
|---|---|---|---|
| RELATED TO ONGOING HEALTH CONDITION? YES / NO | VISIT TO PHYSICIAN / HOSPITAL? | MEDICATION PRESCRIBED: | NOTES: |

| DATE SYMPTOM FIRST STARTED: | NATURE OF SYMPTOM: | MILD MODERATE SEVERE | CONTINUOUS OR INTERMITTENT |
|---|---|---|---|
| RELATED TO ONGOING HEALTH CONDITION? YES / NO | VISIT TO PHYSICIAN / HOSPITAL? | MEDICATION PRESCRIBED: | NOTES: |

# SYMPTOM TRACKER

| DATE SYMPTOM FIRST STARTED: | NATURE OF SYMPTOM: | MILD ☐ <br> MODERATE ☐ <br> SEVERE ☐ | CONTINUOUS OR INTERMITTENT |
|---|---|---|---|
| RELATED TO ONGOING HEALTH CONDITION? <br><br> YES / NO | VISIT TO PHYSICIAN / HOSPITAL? | MEDICATION PRESCRIBED: | NOTES: |

| DATE SYMPTOM FIRST STARTED: | NATURE OF SYMPTOM: | MILD <br> MODERATE <br> SEVERE | CONTINUOUS OR INTERMITTENT |
|---|---|---|---|
| RELATED TO ONGOING HEALTH CONDITION? <br><br> YES / NO | VISIT TO PHYSICIAN / HOSPITAL? | MEDICATION PRESCRIBED: | NOTES: |

| DATE SYMPTOM FIRST STARTED: | NATURE OF SYMPTOM: | MILD <br> MODERATE <br> SEVERE | CONTINUOUS OR INTERMITTENT |
|---|---|---|---|
| RELATED TO ONGOING HEALTH CONDITION? <br><br> YES / NO | VISIT TO PHYSICIAN / HOSPITAL? | MEDICATION PRESCRIBED: | NOTES: |

# SYMPTOM TRACKER

| DATE SYMPTOM FIRST STARTED: | NATURE OF SYMPTOM: | MILD ☐  MODERATE ☐  SEVERE ☐ | CONTINUOUS OR INTERMITTENT |
|---|---|---|---|
| RELATED TO ONGOING HEALTH CONDITION?  YES / NO | VISIT TO PHYSICIAN / HOSPITAL? | MEDICATION PRESCRIBED: | NOTES: |

| DATE SYMPTOM FIRST STARTED: | NATURE OF SYMPTOM: | MILD  MODERATE  SEVERE | CONTINUOUS OR INTERMITTENT |
|---|---|---|---|
| RELATED TO ONGOING HEALTH CONDITION?  YES / NO | VISIT TO PHYSICIAN / HOSPITAL? | MEDICATION PRESCRIBED: | NOTES: |

| DATE SYMPTOM FIRST STARTED: | NATURE OF SYMPTOM: | MILD  MODERATE  SEVERE | CONTINUOUS OR INTERMITTENT |
|---|---|---|---|
| RELATED TO ONGOING HEALTH CONDITION?  YES / NO | VISIT TO PHYSICIAN / HOSPITAL? | MEDICATION PRESCRIBED: | NOTES: |

# SYMPTOM TRACKER

| DATE SYMPTOM FIRST STARTED: | NATURE OF SYMPTOM: | MILD ☐ <br> MODERATE ☐ <br> SEVERE ☐ | CONTINUOUS OR INTERMITTENT |
|---|---|---|---|
| RELATED TO ONGOING HEALTH CONDITION? <br><br> YES / NO | VISIT TO PHYSICIAN / HOSPITAL? | MEDICATION PRESCRIBED: | NOTES: |

| DATE SYMPTOM FIRST STARTED: | NATURE OF SYMPTOM: | MILD <br> MODERATE <br> SEVERE | CONTINUOUS OR INTERMITTENT |
|---|---|---|---|
| RELATED TO ONGOING HEALTH CONDITION? <br><br> YES / NO | VISIT TO PHYSICIAN / HOSPITAL? | MEDICATION PRESCRIBED: | NOTES: |

| DATE SYMPTOM FIRST STARTED: | NATURE OF SYMPTOM: | MILD <br> MODERATE <br> SEVERE | CONTINUOUS OR INTERMITTENT |
|---|---|---|---|
| RELATED TO ONGOING HEALTH CONDITION? <br><br> YES / NO | VISIT TO PHYSICIAN / HOSPITAL? | MEDICATION PRESCRIBED: | NOTES: |

# SYMPTOM TRACKER

| DATE SYMPTOM FIRST STARTED: | NATURE OF SYMPTOM: | MILD ☐ <br> MODERATE ☐ <br> SEVERE ☐ | CONTINUOUS OR INTERMITTENT |
|---|---|---|---|
| RELATED TO ONGOING HEALTH CONDITION? <br><br> YES / NO | VISIT TO PHYSICIAN / HOSPITAL? | MEDICATION PRESCRIBED: | NOTES: |

| DATE SYMPTOM FIRST STARTED: | NATURE OF SYMPTOM: | MILD <br> MODERATE <br> SEVERE | CONTINUOUS OR INTERMITTENT |
|---|---|---|---|
| RELATED TO ONGOING HEALTH CONDITION? <br><br> YES / NO | VISIT TO PHYSICIAN / HOSPITAL? | MEDICATION PRESCRIBED: | NOTES: |

| DATE SYMPTOM FIRST STARTED: | NATURE OF SYMPTOM: | MILD <br> MODERATE <br> SEVERE | CONTINUOUS OR INTERMITTENT |
|---|---|---|---|
| RELATED TO ONGOING HEALTH CONDITION? <br><br> YES / NO | VISIT TO PHYSICIAN / HOSPITAL? | MEDICATION PRESCRIBED: | NOTES: |

# SYMPTOM TRACKER

| DATE SYMPTOM FIRST STARTED: | NATURE OF SYMPTOM: | MILD ☐ MODERATE ☐ SEVERE ☐ | CONTINUOUS OR INTERMITTENT |
|---|---|---|---|
| RELATED TO ONGOING HEALTH CONDITION? <br><br> YES / NO | VISIT TO PHYSICIAN / HOSPITAL? | MEDICATION PRESCRIBED: | NOTES: |

| DATE SYMPTOM FIRST STARTED: | NATURE OF SYMPTOM: | MILD <br> MODERATE <br> SEVERE | CONTINUOUS OR INTERMITTENT |
|---|---|---|---|
| RELATED TO ONGOING HEALTH CONDITION? <br><br> YES / NO | VISIT TO PHYSICIAN / HOSPITAL? | MEDICATION PRESCRIBED: | NOTES: |

| DATE SYMPTOM FIRST STARTED: | NATURE OF SYMPTOM: | MILD <br> MODERATE <br> SEVERE | CONTINUOUS OR INTERMITTENT |
|---|---|---|---|
| RELATED TO ONGOING HEALTH CONDITION? <br><br> YES / NO | VISIT TO PHYSICIAN / HOSPITAL? | MEDICATION PRESCRIBED: | NOTES: |

# SYMPTOM TRACKER

| DATE SYMPTOM FIRST STARTED: | NATURE OF SYMPTOM: | MILD ☐ MODERATE ☐ SEVERE ☐ | CONTINUOUS OR INTERMITTENT |
|---|---|---|---|
| RELATED TO ONGOING HEALTH CONDITION? YES / NO | VISIT TO PHYSICIAN / HOSPITAL? | MEDICATION PRESCRIBED: | NOTES: |

| DATE SYMPTOM FIRST STARTED: | NATURE OF SYMPTOM: | MILD MODERATE SEVERE | CONTINUOUS OR INTERMITTENT |
|---|---|---|---|
| RELATED TO ONGOING HEALTH CONDITION? YES / NO | VISIT TO PHYSICIAN / HOSPITAL? | MEDICATION PRESCRIBED: | NOTES: |

| DATE SYMPTOM FIRST STARTED: | NATURE OF SYMPTOM: | MILD MODERATE SEVERE | CONTINUOUS OR INTERMITTENT |
|---|---|---|---|
| RELATED TO ONGOING HEALTH CONDITION? YES / NO | VISIT TO PHYSICIAN / HOSPITAL? | MEDICATION PRESCRIBED: | NOTES: |

# SYMPTOM TRACKER

| DATE SYMPTOM FIRST STARTED: | NATURE OF SYMPTOM: | MILD ☐ MODERATE ☐ SEVERE ☐ | CONTINUOUS OR INTERMITTENT |
|---|---|---|---|
| RELATED TO ONGOING HEALTH CONDITION? YES / NO | VISIT TO PHYSICIAN / HOSPITAL? | MEDICATION PRESCRIBED: | NOTES: |

| DATE SYMPTOM FIRST STARTED: | NATURE OF SYMPTOM: | MILD MODERATE SEVERE | CONTINUOUS OR INTERMITTENT |
|---|---|---|---|
| RELATED TO ONGOING HEALTH CONDITION? YES / NO | VISIT TO PHYSICIAN / HOSPITAL? | MEDICATION PRESCRIBED: | NOTES: |

| DATE SYMPTOM FIRST STARTED: | NATURE OF SYMPTOM: | MILD MODERATE SEVERE | CONTINUOUS OR INTERMITTENT |
|---|---|---|---|
| RELATED TO ONGOING HEALTH CONDITION? YES / NO | VISIT TO PHYSICIAN / HOSPITAL? | MEDICATION PRESCRIBED: | NOTES: |

# SYMPTOM TRACKER

| DATE SYMPTOM FIRST STARTED: | NATURE OF SYMPTOM: | MILD ☐ <br> MODERATE ☐ <br> SEVERE ☐ | CONTINUOUS OR INTERMITTENT |
|---|---|---|---|
| RELATED TO ONGOING HEALTH CONDITION? <br><br> YES / NO | VISIT TO PHYSICIAN / HOSPITAL? | MEDICATION PRESCRIBED: | NOTES: |

| DATE SYMPTOM FIRST STARTED: | NATURE OF SYMPTOM: | MILD <br> MODERATE <br> SEVERE | CONTINUOUS OR INTERMITTENT |
|---|---|---|---|
| RELATED TO ONGOING HEALTH CONDITION? <br><br> YES / NO | VISIT TO PHYSICIAN / HOSPITAL? | MEDICATION PRESCRIBED: | NOTES: |

| DATE SYMPTOM FIRST STARTED: | NATURE OF SYMPTOM: | MILD <br> MODERATE <br> SEVERE | CONTINUOUS OR INTERMITTENT |
|---|---|---|---|
| RELATED TO ONGOING HEALTH CONDITION? <br><br> YES / NO | VISIT TO PHYSICIAN / HOSPITAL? | MEDICATION PRESCRIBED: | NOTES: |

# SYMPTOM TRACKER

| DATE SYMPTOM FIRST STARTED: | NATURE OF SYMPTOM: | MILD ☐ MODERATE ☐ SEVERE ☐ | CONTINUOUS OR INTERMITTENT |
|---|---|---|---|
| RELATED TO ONGOING HEALTH CONDITION?<br><br>YES / NO | VISIT TO PHYSICIAN / HOSPITAL? | MEDICATION PRESCRIBED: | NOTES: |

| DATE SYMPTOM FIRST STARTED: | NATURE OF SYMPTOM: | MILD<br><br>MODERATE<br><br>SEVERE | CONTINUOUS OR INTERMITTENT |
|---|---|---|---|
| RELATED TO ONGOING HEALTH CONDITION?<br><br>YES / NO | VISIT TO PHYSICIAN / HOSPITAL? | MEDICATION PRESCRIBED: | NOTES: |

| DATE SYMPTOM FIRST STARTED: | NATURE OF SYMPTOM: | MILD<br><br>MODERATE<br><br>SEVERE | CONTINUOUS OR INTERMITTENT |
|---|---|---|---|
| RELATED TO ONGOING HEALTH CONDITION?<br><br>YES / NO | VISIT TO PHYSICIAN / HOSPITAL? | MEDICATION PRESCRIBED: | NOTES: |

# SYMPTOM TRACKER

| DATE SYMPTOM FIRST STARTED: | NATURE OF SYMPTOM: | MILD ☐ <br> MODERATE ☐ <br> SEVERE ☐ | CONTINUOUS OR INTERMITTENT |
|---|---|---|---|
| RELATED TO ONGOING HEALTH CONDITION? <br><br> YES / NO | VISIT TO PHYSICIAN / HOSPITAL? | MEDICATION PRESCRIBED: | NOTES: |

| DATE SYMPTOM FIRST STARTED: | NATURE OF SYMPTOM: | MILD <br> MODERATE <br> SEVERE | CONTINUOUS OR INTERMITTENT |
|---|---|---|---|
| RELATED TO ONGOING HEALTH CONDITION? <br><br> YES / NO | VISIT TO PHYSICIAN / HOSPITAL? | MEDICATION PRESCRIBED: | NOTES: |

| DATE SYMPTOM FIRST STARTED: | NATURE OF SYMPTOM: | MILD <br> MODERATE <br> SEVERE | CONTINUOUS OR INTERMITTENT |
|---|---|---|---|
| RELATED TO ONGOING HEALTH CONDITION? <br><br> YES / NO | VISIT TO PHYSICIAN / HOSPITAL? | MEDICATION PRESCRIBED: | NOTES: |

# SYMPTOM TRACKER

| DATE SYMPTOM FIRST STARTED: | NATURE OF SYMPTOM: | MILD ☐ MODERATE ☐ SEVERE ☐ | CONTINUOUS OR INTERMITTENT |
|---|---|---|---|
| RELATED TO ONGOING HEALTH CONDITION? YES / NO | VISIT TO PHYSICIAN / HOSPITAL? | MEDICATION PRESCRIBED: | NOTES: |

| DATE SYMPTOM FIRST STARTED: | NATURE OF SYMPTOM: | MILD MODERATE SEVERE | CONTINUOUS OR INTERMITTENT |
|---|---|---|---|
| RELATED TO ONGOING HEALTH CONDITION? YES / NO | VISIT TO PHYSICIAN / HOSPITAL? | MEDICATION PRESCRIBED: | NOTES: |

| DATE SYMPTOM FIRST STARTED: | NATURE OF SYMPTOM: | MILD MODERATE SEVERE | CONTINUOUS OR INTERMITTENT |
|---|---|---|---|
| RELATED TO ONGOING HEALTH CONDITION? YES / NO | VISIT TO PHYSICIAN / HOSPITAL? | MEDICATION PRESCRIBED: | NOTES: |

# SYMPTOM TRACKER

| DATE SYMPTOM FIRST STARTED: | NATURE OF SYMPTOM: | MILD ☐ MODERATE ☐ SEVERE ☐ | CONTINUOUS OR INTERMITTENT |
|---|---|---|---|
| RELATED TO ONGOING HEALTH CONDITION? YES / NO | VISIT TO PHYSICIAN / HOSPITAL? | MEDICATION PRESCRIBED: | NOTES: |

| DATE SYMPTOM FIRST STARTED: | NATURE OF SYMPTOM: | MILD MODERATE SEVERE | CONTINUOUS OR INTERMITTENT |
|---|---|---|---|
| RELATED TO ONGOING HEALTH CONDITION? YES / NO | VISIT TO PHYSICIAN / HOSPITAL? | MEDICATION PRESCRIBED: | NOTES: |

| DATE SYMPTOM FIRST STARTED: | NATURE OF SYMPTOM: | MILD MODERATE SEVERE | CONTINUOUS OR INTERMITTENT |
|---|---|---|---|
| RELATED TO ONGOING HEALTH CONDITION? YES / NO | VISIT TO PHYSICIAN / HOSPITAL? | MEDICATION PRESCRIBED: | NOTES: |

# SYMPTOM TRACKER

| DATE SYMPTOM FIRST STARTED: | NATURE OF SYMPTOM: | MILD ☐ <br><br> MODERATE ☐ <br><br> SEVERE ☐ | CONTINUOUS OR INTERMITTENT |
|---|---|---|---|
| RELATED TO ONGOING HEALTH CONDITION? <br><br> YES / NO | VISIT TO PHYSICIAN / HOSPITAL? | MEDICATION PRESCRIBED: | NOTES: |

| DATE SYMPTOM FIRST STARTED: | NATURE OF SYMPTOM: | MILD <br><br> MODERATE <br><br> SEVERE | CONTINUOUS OR INTERMITTENT |
|---|---|---|---|
| RELATED TO ONGOING HEALTH CONDITION? <br><br> YES / NO | VISIT TO PHYSICIAN / HOSPITAL? | MEDICATION PRESCRIBED: | NOTES: |

| DATE SYMPTOM FIRST STARTED: | NATURE OF SYMPTOM: | MILD <br><br> MODERATE <br><br> SEVERE | CONTINUOUS OR INTERMITTENT |
|---|---|---|---|
| RELATED TO ONGOING HEALTH CONDITION? <br><br> YES / NO | VISIT TO PHYSICIAN / HOSPITAL? | MEDICATION PRESCRIBED: | NOTES: |

# SYMPTOM TRACKER

| DATE SYMPTOM FIRST STARTED: | NATURE OF SYMPTOM: | MILD ☐  MODERATE ☐  SEVERE ☐ | CONTINUOUS OR INTERMITTENT |
|---|---|---|---|
| RELATED TO ONGOING HEALTH CONDITION?  YES / NO | VISIT TO PHYSICIAN / HOSPITAL? | MEDICATION PRESCRIBED: | NOTES: |

| DATE SYMPTOM FIRST STARTED: | NATURE OF SYMPTOM: | MILD  MODERATE  SEVERE | CONTINUOUS OR INTERMITTENT |
|---|---|---|---|
| RELATED TO ONGOING HEALTH CONDITION?  YES / NO | VISIT TO PHYSICIAN / HOSPITAL? | MEDICATION PRESCRIBED: | NOTES: |

| DATE SYMPTOM FIRST STARTED: | NATURE OF SYMPTOM: | MILD  MODERATE  SEVERE | CONTINUOUS OR INTERMITTENT |
|---|---|---|---|
| RELATED TO ONGOING HEALTH CONDITION?  YES / NO | VISIT TO PHYSICIAN / HOSPITAL? | MEDICATION PRESCRIBED: | NOTES: |

# SYMPTOM TRACKER

| DATE SYMPTOM FIRST STARTED: | NATURE OF SYMPTOM: | MILD ☐ <br> MODERATE ☐ <br> SEVERE ☐ | CONTINUOUS OR INTERMITTENT |
|---|---|---|---|
| RELATED TO ONGOING HEALTH CONDITION? <br><br> YES / NO | VISIT TO PHYSICIAN / HOSPITAL? | MEDICATION PRESCRIBED: | NOTES: |

| DATE SYMPTOM FIRST STARTED: | NATURE OF SYMPTOM: | MILD <br> MODERATE <br> SEVERE | CONTINUOUS OR INTERMITTENT |
|---|---|---|---|
| RELATED TO ONGOING HEALTH CONDITION? <br><br> YES / NO | VISIT TO PHYSICIAN / HOSPITAL? | MEDICATION PRESCRIBED: | NOTES: |

| DATE SYMPTOM FIRST STARTED: | NATURE OF SYMPTOM: | MILD <br> MODERATE <br> SEVERE | CONTINUOUS OR INTERMITTENT |
|---|---|---|---|
| RELATED TO ONGOING HEALTH CONDITION? <br><br> YES / NO | VISIT TO PHYSICIAN / HOSPITAL? | MEDICATION PRESCRIBED: | NOTES: |

# SYMPTOM TRACKER

| DATE SYMPTOM FIRST STARTED: | NATURE OF SYMPTOM: | MILD ☐  MODERATE ☐  SEVERE ☐ | CONTINUOUS OR INTERMITTENT |
|---|---|---|---|
| RELATED TO ONGOING HEALTH CONDITION?  YES / NO | VISIT TO PHYSICIAN / HOSPITAL? | MEDICATION PRESCRIBED: | NOTES: |

| DATE SYMPTOM FIRST STARTED: | NATURE OF SYMPTOM: | MILD  MODERATE  SEVERE | CONTINUOUS OR INTERMITTENT |
|---|---|---|---|
| RELATED TO ONGOING HEALTH CONDITION?  YES / NO | VISIT TO PHYSICIAN / HOSPITAL? | MEDICATION PRESCRIBED: | NOTES: |

| DATE SYMPTOM FIRST STARTED: | NATURE OF SYMPTOM: | MILD  MODERATE  SEVERE | CONTINUOUS OR INTERMITTENT |
|---|---|---|---|
| RELATED TO ONGOING HEALTH CONDITION?  YES / NO | VISIT TO PHYSICIAN / HOSPITAL? | MEDICATION PRESCRIBED: | NOTES: |

# SYMPTOM TRACKER

| DATE SYMPTOM FIRST STARTED: | NATURE OF SYMPTOM: | MILD ☐ <br> MODERATE ☐ <br> SEVERE ☐ | CONTINUOUS OR INTERMITTENT |
|---|---|---|---|
| RELATED TO ONGOING HEALTH CONDITION? <br><br> YES / NO | VISIT TO PHYSICIAN / HOSPITAL? | MEDICATION PRESCRIBED: | NOTES: |

| DATE SYMPTOM FIRST STARTED: | NATURE OF SYMPTOM: | MILD <br> MODERATE <br> SEVERE | CONTINUOUS OR INTERMITTENT |
|---|---|---|---|
| RELATED TO ONGOING HEALTH CONDITION? <br><br> YES / NO | VISIT TO PHYSICIAN / HOSPITAL? | MEDICATION PRESCRIBED: | NOTES: |

| DATE SYMPTOM FIRST STARTED: | NATURE OF SYMPTOM: | MILD <br> MODERATE <br> SEVERE | CONTINUOUS OR INTERMITTENT |
|---|---|---|---|
| RELATED TO ONGOING HEALTH CONDITION? <br><br> YES / NO | VISIT TO PHYSICIAN / HOSPITAL? | MEDICATION PRESCRIBED: | NOTES: |

# BLOOD PRESSURE LOG

| DATE: | TIME: | BLOOD PRESSURE: | PULSE: |
|-------|-------|-----------------|--------|
|       |       |                 |        |
|       |       |                 |        |
|       |       |                 |        |
|       |       |                 |        |
|       |       |                 |        |
|       |       |                 |        |
|       |       |                 |        |
|       |       |                 |        |
|       |       |                 |        |
|       |       |                 |        |
|       |       |                 |        |
|       |       |                 |        |
|       |       |                 |        |
|       |       |                 |        |
|       |       |                 |        |
|       |       |                 |        |
|       |       |                 |        |
|       |       |                 |        |

# BLOOD PRESSURE LOG

| DATE: | TIME: | BLOOD PRESSURE: | PULSE: |
|-------|-------|-----------------|--------|
|       |       |                 |        |
|       |       |                 |        |
|       |       |                 |        |
|       |       |                 |        |
|       |       |                 |        |
|       |       |                 |        |
|       |       |                 |        |
|       |       |                 |        |
|       |       |                 |        |
|       |       |                 |        |
|       |       |                 |        |
|       |       |                 |        |
|       |       |                 |        |
|       |       |                 |        |
|       |       |                 |        |
|       |       |                 |        |
|       |       |                 |        |
|       |       |                 |        |
|       |       |                 |        |
|       |       |                 |        |
|       |       |                 |        |

# BLOOD PRESSURE LOG

| DATE: | TIME: | BLOOD PRESSURE: | PULSE: |
|-------|-------|-----------------|--------|
|       |       |                 |        |
|       |       |                 |        |
|       |       |                 |        |
|       |       |                 |        |
|       |       |                 |        |
|       |       |                 |        |
|       |       |                 |        |
|       |       |                 |        |
|       |       |                 |        |
|       |       |                 |        |
|       |       |                 |        |
|       |       |                 |        |
|       |       |                 |        |
|       |       |                 |        |
|       |       |                 |        |
|       |       |                 |        |
|       |       |                 |        |
|       |       |                 |        |
|       |       |                 |        |
|       |       |                 |        |

# MEDICAL EXPENSES

**YEAR:**

| DATE: | DESCRIPTION: | INSURANCE %: | COST: |
|-------|-------------|-------------|-------|
|  |  |  |  |
|  |  |  |  |
|  |  |  |  |
|  |  |  |  |
|  |  |  |  |
|  |  |  |  |
|  |  |  |  |
|  |  |  |  |
|  |  |  |  |
|  |  |  |  |
|  |  |  |  |
|  |  |  |  |
|  |  |  |  |
|  |  |  |  |
|  |  |  |  |
|  |  |  |  |
|  |  |  |  |
|  |  |  |  |
|  |  |  |  |
|  |  |  |  |
|  |  |  |  |
|  |  |  |  |

# MEDICAL EXPENSES

YEAR:

| DATE: | DESCRIPTION: | INSURANCE %: | COST: |
|-------|--------------|--------------|-------|
| | | | |
| | | | |
| | | | |
| | | | |
| | | | |
| | | | |
| | | | |
| | | | |
| | | | |
| | | | |
| | | | |
| | | | |
| | | | |
| | | | |
| | | | |
| | | | |
| | | | |
| | | | |
| | | | |

# MEDICAL EXPENSES

YEAR:

| DATE: | DESCRIPTION: | INSURANCE %: | COST: |
|-------|--------------|--------------|-------|
|       |              |              |       |
|       |              |              |       |
|       |              |              |       |
|       |              |              |       |
|       |              |              |       |
|       |              |              |       |
|       |              |              |       |
|       |              |              |       |
|       |              |              |       |
|       |              |              |       |
|       |              |              |       |
|       |              |              |       |
|       |              |              |       |
|       |              |              |       |
|       |              |              |       |
|       |              |              |       |
|       |              |              |       |
|       |              |              |       |
|       |              |              |       |

# ADDITIONAL NOTES

# ADDITIONAL NOTES

# ADDITIONAL NOTES

# ADDITIONAL NOTES

# ADDITIONAL NOTES

# ADDITIONAL NOTES

# ADDITIONAL NOTES

# ADDITIONAL NOTES

# ADDITIONAL NOTES

# ADDITIONAL NOTES

# ADDITIONAL NOTES

# ADDITIONAL NOTES

# ADDITIONAL NOTES

# ADDITIONAL NOTES

# ADDITIONAL NOTES

# ADDITIONAL NOTES

# Thank you for using this Personal Health Record Log Book

I sincerely hope that you have found it useful and easy to use. Please leave me a Review on Amazon – I would really appreciate it.

Simply find this Journal –

*"Personal Health Record Log Book – My Medical Journal"*
*by Medical Journals.*

Scroll down to the 'Leave Review' Link and let me know what you think.

Thank you so much for your time.

Made in United States
Orlando, FL
13 February 2023